Hike to l

STROLLING WITH JOHN

by

JOHN N. MERRILL

Photographs and illustrations by John N. Merrill

a J.N.M. PUBLICATION

Happy walking!

John N. Merrill

1987

a J.N.M. PUBLICATION

JNM PUBLICATIONS,
WINSTER,
MATLOCK,
DERBYSHIRE.
DE4 2DQ

Conceived, edited, typeset, designed, marketed and distributed by John N. Merrill.

© Text — John N. Merrill 1985 and 1987

© Illustrations and photographs — John N. Merrill 1987

First Published — February 1985

This enlarged edition — July 1987

ISBN 0 907496 51 2

Meticulous research has been undertaken to ensure that this publication is highly accurate at the time of going to press. The publishers, however, cannot be held responsible for alterations, errors or omissions, but they would welcome notification of such for future editions.

Printed by: Commercial Colour Press, London E7 0EW.

ABOUT JOHN N. MERRILL

John combines the characteristics and strength of a mountain climber with the stamina and athletic capabilities of a marathon runner. In this respect he is unique and has to his credit a whole string of remarkable long walks. He is without question the world's leading marathon walker.

Over the last ten years he has walked more than 60,000 miles and successfully completed ten walks of at least 1,000 miles or more.

His six major walks in Great Britain are —
Hebridean Journey.. 1,003 miles
Northern Isles Journey ....913 miles
Irish Island Journey.. 1,578 miles
Parkland Journey.. 2,043 miles
Lands End to John o'Groats ....1,608 miles
and in 1978 he became the first person (permanent Guinness Book of Records entry) to walk the entire coastline of Britain — 6,824 miles in ten months.

In Europe he has walked across Austria — 712 miles, hiked the Tour of Mont Blanc, completed High Level Routes in the Dolomites, and the GR20 route across Corsica in training! In 1982 he walked across Europe — 2,806 miles in 107 days — crossing seven countries, the Swiss and French Alps and the complete Pyrennean chain — the hardest and longest mountain walk in Europe with more than 600,000 feet of ascent!

In America he used the the world's longest footpath — The Appalachian Trail — 2,200 miles — as a training walk. He has walked from Mexico to Canada via the Pacific Crest Trail in record time — 118 days for 2,700 miles.

During the summer of 1984, John set off from Virginia Beach on the Atlantic coast, and walked 4,226 miles without a rest day, across the width of America to Santa Cruz and San Francisco on the Pacific Ocean. his walk is unquestionably his greatest achievement, being, in modern history, the longest, hardest crossing of the USA in the shortest time — under six months (178 days). The direct distance is 2,800 miles.

Between major walks John is out training in his own area — the Peak District National Park. As well as walking in other parts of Britain and Europe he has been trekking in the Himalayas five times. He has created more than ten challenge walks which have been used to raise more than £250,000 for charity. From his own walks he raised over £80,000. He is author of more than seventy books, many of which he publishes himself. His next major walk — 2.400 miles — is down the length of New Zealand.

CONTENTS

INTRODUCTION

We are lucky in Britain that surrounding our cities and towns is a most diverse variety of countryside. Here you can get away from the pace of modern life and see your surroundings on their own terms.

Walking is the most natural way to keep fit and healthy. It is the only "sport" that can be enjoyed all life long. The principal attraction of walking in the countryside is that it can be made interesting, educational and informative. Here you can observe the birds and wild flowers; learn the geology of the area, and explore historical buildings and churches. This all gives added impetus to taking a walk, keeping fit in the process, while learning about your environment.

You don't have to walk far — 3 to 5 miles will bring you into attractive scenery, historical buildings and nature. My day walk guide books have set a trend by being circular, high in interest, having clear maps, historical notes and a pub for lunch! The essence of countryside walking is not distance but getting out and seeing at close hand, for yourself, its characteristics.

I have tried running as a means to keep in reasonable shape for my long walks, but I have found I became unusually tired and the constant pounding of the joints and muscles made me stiff and sore. I am convinced that the best way to keep fit is by walking, which is the kindest form of exercise for your body.

In this book I have drawn on my walking experience and knowledge to explain the basics of walking. I hope you are encouraged to put on a pair of boots and explore the countryside regularly and see what lies on your doorstep, while keeping fit and healthy.

Happy walking!

JOHN N. MERRILL

WINSTER 1987

1

ABOUT WALKING

Usually I walk alone, not because I am anti-social but simply because I can go where I want, when I want. While walking I am busy thinking over problems and decisions; for walking is a brain-stimulating exercise away from the normal stresses of life. The other side of walking is with a group, which is most enjoyable for as you chat away you learn about your companions, their thoughts and aspirations. You can also discuss your own problems and often find a solution.

Walking is not just for comradeship but a means to see the world at its own pace and terms. To wander down a country lane and see the birds in the trees, the wild flowers in the hedgerows, and the wild life scampering away at your approach is one of the joys of living. If you carry the relative guidebook you can look up the flower name and learn about its habitat and uses, increasing your knowledge of your environment.

The other major aspect of walking is health and fitness. It is agreed that walking just a mile a day is far more beneficial to you than a weekly jog or a game of tennis. Furthermore it is far less harmful to your muscles, joints and tendons than running. Walking exercises and uses far more muscles than the majority of outdoor activities and gives your whole body a much better usage. While walking you use more than half the body's 650 muscles and 200 bones. You will breathe more easily, sleep better, and have a fine complexion superior to any make-up!

Walking is not really a way to slim, for you will have to walk consistently very far and over a long period to show any substantial weight loss. On my recent walk across America I lost 30 pounds after walking 4,226 miles in 178 days! You will have to walk about 40 miles in a day to lose a pound in weight. Walking is a very gradual way to lose weight but will tone your muscles up, reduce flab and make you feel and look healthy.

As a guideline, if you walk three miles every day you will lose:–

1 lb. in 7 days
5 lb. in 35 days
10 lbs. in 70 days
20 lbs. in 140 days

If you walk six miles every day you will lose:–

1 lb. in 5 days
5 lbs. in 27 days
10 lbs. in 54 days
20 lbs. in 108 days

The above is based on an average person weighing 150 pounds who walks at the rate of 3 miles per hour and will use 260 calories—approximately 87 calories a mile. If you are carrying a 20 lb. rucksack you will use 312 calories an hour, and a 40 lb. load, 348 calories.

As a basic guide to how much ground an average adult can cover, W. Naismith, founder of the Scottish Mountaineering Club, created the following formula:–

2

John Merrill on the Summit of Sunrise Mountain — 14,000 ft., Colorado, U.S.A.

On reasonably level terrain –
3 m.p.h. (5 km. p.h.) when carrying no equipment.
2½ m.p.h. (4 km. p.h.) when carrying equipment.

In mountains:–
1,000 ft. (300 m.) ascend without equipment in half an hour.
750 ft. (225 m.) ascend with equipment in half an hour.
Young children usually average 2½ m.p.h. or ascend 750 ft. without equipment.

When walking, adopt a steady pace that you feel happy with and one where you are not forcing yourself. You should be reasonably fresh at the end of the walk and still be able to walk further. There is no point in rushing at the start and being tired for the rest of the day. Your pace should suit you individually, although this is hard when in a group, for if you walk slower or faster than normal you will be more tired at the end of the day than your companions.

Hills are always a problem, and I believe there is only one real way to tackle them, and that is by constant walking. Adopt a steady, slow pace that you can keep up and simply keep going. There are two reasons for this. One, you get into a steady rhythm and, secondly, this helps psychologically — you are soon on the summit, usually quicker than you thought. If you stop and rest this breaks your rhythm and concentration and makes the ascent seem very long. This could demoralise you and make you want to give up.

Basically you must adapt your walking pace and speed to the area you are walking in. On the flat you can keep up a steady pace and average upto 4 m.p.h.. In the mountains you ascend steadily but can descend quite fast. In alpine conditions your pace will be slower because of the altitude. Whatever you do don't force it, just walk to enjoy the surroundings.

3

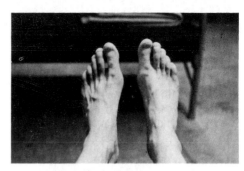
Author's Feet

YOUR FEET

It is perhaps amazing to realise that an average person walks 70,000 miles in their lifetime. And for every mile walked your leg muscles will have flexed a minimum of 1,500 times. This adds up to 105,000,000 minimum flexes in a lifetime! Equally disturbing is the fact that most of us take our feet for granted. They take considerable punishment when walking, and are one of the most complicated parts of the body with twenty-six bones.

On my long walks I have suffered from three stress fractures in my foot metatarsals; simply because I had walked too much in too short a time -upto 40 miles everyday with no rest days, carrying about 50 to 60 pounds of equipment on my back. This is unlikely to happen to you! The most common foot ailment is blisters. I always wear two pairs of thick socks inside my boots with a foam insole. This helps to cushion the base of your foot and form a cushioning layer all round, minimising rubbing. Despite these precautions blisters develop even when wearing well-broken-in boots.

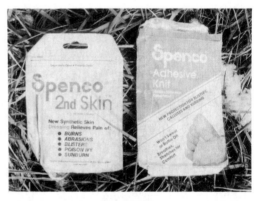
Second Skin

BLISTERS

How you treat blisters is a very controversial subject. Many use moleskin or 'second skin' over the afflicted area, and these generally relieve the situation. For a long while I left my blisters alone, letting them take their course. At night I would walk around barefoot and let the air get at them and help to dry them out. More recently I have adopted the principle that it is best to burst them with a sterilized needle, and squeeze as much fluid out as possible and let the air dry them out. I am always very reluctant to put a plaster over them, for from experience I have never been successful, ending up with a much bigger blister. If covering a blister it is best to be very generous and cover at least twice the area.

EQUIPMENT—BOOTS/FOOTWEAR.

The 1980's have seen a revolution in the accepted form of boots for walking. Up to this time boots were made from leather with a commando/vibram rubber sole. Generally they weighed from 3 lbs. to 5 lbs. a pair, and are known today as "heavyweight" or "traditional" boots. For many years no one questioned their weight or suitability for countryside walking. The traditional boots needed a lot of wear before moulding themselves to your feet and becoming blister free. My boots have often needed to be used about 500 miles before they felt comfortable and fully broken-in. The lightweight leather boot needs very little breaking in. After becoming wet a couple of times they will be fitting like gloves.

During these last few years boots have been studied in very great depth:- Are they too heavy? Can we use lighter and synthetic materials? Is the sole the right design? How can we reduce the breaking-in period? With these questions in mind "lightweight" boots began emerging on the market. First as a trickle, then in huge quantities. Most have a so-called environment sole, which is said to safeguard the terrain by reducing countryside erosion. To make them lightweight the uppers instead of leather are a mixture of suede and cordura or polyurethane-coated nylon. A pair weighs little more than two pounds. Having now used more than a dozen pairs of different types of lightweight boots, I have come to the following conclusions.

I have found the environmental sole to wear much quicker than the traditional vibram sole. I have no evidence either way on whether it reduces countryside wear, but I do know the sole clogs up much quicker in muddy terrain than vibram. To make a boot lightweight the uppers are of light synthetic materials. Whilst they may look aesthetically attractive at first they are hard to keep clean. And if you spend all day in wet conditions your feet remain wet all day as well. Waxing is a problem, and spraying only makes them waterproof for a few hours.

Inside the boots are a variety of insoles which help to reduce the shock of foot travel on the ground. To a certain extent they cushion too much, and I often have blisters at the end of the day. As far as I am concerned, a lightweight boot does not do what a boot is designed to do. First it should cushion you from the ground. Secondly it should provide ankle support. I agree that a lighter boot is more suitable for day walking, but it must also keep you dry.

Leather Lightweight Boots

5

I therefore for day walks use a medium-weight leather upper boot with a vibram sole. They are easy to keep clean, support my ankles and, by inserting a foam insole, cushion my feet from the ground. The boots weigh 3 lbs.. Many people venture into the hills in training shoes. They may be comfortable but are totally unsuitable, being non-supportive, non-waterproof, and having a very poor gripping sole. In bad weather they are quite lethal. Plastic boots are now on the market, and ski boots, which were once made of leather, are now all plastic. This is fine for downhill skiing, where rigidity is necessary. But a walking boot must flex and breathe. So far I have tried three pairs of plastic boots and have been quite impressed. They are light, waterproof and flex well, and could well be suitable footwear for day walking.

Plastic Walking Boots

CARE OF YOUR BOOTS

After your walk clean the mud off them and prise out any stones lodged in the sole. If wet dry well away from the fire and insert newspaper inside. Peronally I use Neatsfoot Oil, which nourishes the leather, makes the boot more supple, and, unlike a wax, which stays on the surface, soaks into the leather. It is now being realised that the sweat inside the boot is harmful to the leather, and a special wax is being produced for this.

SOCKS

Inside the boots I wear two pairs of thick socks; generally made of 80% wool. Two pairs give extra cushioning to your feet and help minimise rubbing which leads to blisters. The inner sock is of loop-stitch construction — most kind to your feet. The outer is a more durable rib-wool sock.

GAITERS

Many people wear these all year round, but they are most useful in winter conditions, keeping snow from entering the top of your boot. Basically, a gaiter is made of nylon, cordura or heavy-duty cotton. At the front a clip hooks onto your front lace and a strap or cord goes underneath your instep. At the back is a full-length zip with a draw cord at the top, for securing beneath your knee. I have rarely used them, for I find them a nuisance to put on and, once on, they are messy to undo. Again I go for freedom and hate being too enclosed, preferring to do without and feel comfortable.

"Heavyweight" Boots

After 1,000 Miles

John Merrill in Summer Walking Gear

CLOTHING

The clothes you wear must be ones that you feel comfortable in, and will vary according to the seasons. During the summer I wear just T-shirts, and in winter long trousers and fibre-pile jackets.

SHORTS AND TROUSERS

Personally, I wear shorts from May to October. Always made from 100% cotton, I alternate between a simple pair of running shorts to ones with side and hip pockets. My preference for shorts stems from the greater freedom of movement and the 'clammy' feeling inside long trousers as you ascend a hill. My legs never feel cold. During early summer or autumn, I will often walk in a track suit or thin cotton long trousers.

Winter time is a different matter, where cold soon strikes the improperly clad. Never wear jeans, for they are totally unsuitable and when wet lose their heat retention effectiveness and can start hypothermia. It is far wiser to wear a pair of corduroy trousers or special walking trousers made from a wool or cotton mixture. Another equally useful trouser wear is walking/climbing breeches. Again made from woollen or cotton mixture, they have the advantage of being only just below the knee length. This allows greater freedom of movement than long trousers, and instead of having your long socks to your knees you can push them down to your ankles and can control your heat. Again there are lightweight cotton breeches for summer and heavier cloths for winter use. Many now are made from elasticated fabrics.

What clothing you wear is, of course, a very personal matter, and we all have different tastes and colour sense. These notes are simply a guide to what I wear and why.

SHIRTS

For a long while I used to wear thick cotton shirts with two breast pockets. The pockets were useful, but I wanted less restriction and short sleeves, and for the last seven years I have worn just T-shirts during the summer. They are light and easy to wash, and allow my arms to tan! In the cooler months I revert back to a thick cotton shirt. Many wear thick woollen shirts, but I have never felt comfortable in them.

PULLOVERS

Again because I dislike the enclosed feeling, I very rarely wear a crew-neck sweater, much preferring a simple V-neck sweater. I usually carry a medium-weight one in case of cooler weather or emergency. Fibre-pile and fleece jackets have become extremely popular over the last decade, and have the advantage of a full-length zip, allowing you to ventilate and control your heat. More recently jackets made from better materials, more windproof and more comfortable, and which do not 'pill', have come onto the market.

WINDJACKET

I find a thigh-length jacket most useful. Made from cotton or a mixture of fibres, the jackets are windproof and light. They have at least four pockets, waist draw-cord and hood, either attached or in the collar. The pockets are useful for keeping map and compass and snacks. But primarily they are most useful for keeping warm in mild conditions. A T-shirt and waist or thigh length jacket are just right for the mountains in summertime.

LAYERING

The last three items of clothing are most suitable for the layering principle. Experience has shown that, wearing several layers of clothes, the body retains its heat far more than if you were wearing just a T-shirt and down-filled jacket. The principal advantage, since warm air is trapped between the layers, is that by adding or subtracting a layer you can control your heat and feel comfortable all the time.

WATERPROOFS

Today there is a bewildering assortment of equipment on the market, made from a variety of "waterproof" cloths. The most popular are polyurethane-coated nylon; some are neoprene-coated for better bonding. The only drawback with these materials is, they do keep water out but are non-breathable, causing considerable sweating inside — often becoming equally wet inside as outside.

In an effort to overcome the "clammy" feeling, several new "breathable" cloths have come onto the market. These all react differently to individual wearers, depending on your walking speed, normal body heat and how much heat you generate. A nylon-coated jacket costs up to £40, and a "breathable" jacket up to £100.

Personally I feel most comfortable in a cotton windproof jacket. If it rains hard I put on a nylon cagoule. In a downpour I put on overtrousers.

Waterproof Jacket/Cagoule

Full-length zip — which allows ventilation — with covering flap sealed by velcro. Two lower pockets and a map pocket at chest level. The sleeves have either elasticated or knitted cuffs. An integral hood with draw-cords covers the head and, on the more expensive models, a wired hood.

Waterproof Overtrousers

Elasticated waist with tapered trousers. Some have pocket slits for access to your inside trouser pockets. The bottoms are usually zipped, with an 18 inch zip to allow easy fitting over your boots. Most have a gusset behind the zip, making them more water-repellent. More expensive models have a full-length zip from waist to boot for ease of putting on.

Winter Walking Gear

FOUR SEASON WEAR

Whilst you will be using all the above clothing all year, you will need additional clothing for the cooler months, to ensure your safety and warmth.

HATS

Many wear hats all year round. Personally I dislike anything on my head, but with thinning hair on top I have to wear a cap in constant sunny conditions! Surprisingly, you lose 30% of your heat through your head, so a hat is very important. A woollen bob or ski hat is ideal as this will keep our head, forehead and ears warm. For more exposed mountain walking a balaclava is essential. Apart from being a woollen hat, you can pull it down to cover your face, leaving only your eyes and nose exposed.

GLOVES

There is nothing more uncomfortable than having cold, throbbing hands. Whilst woollen gloves give warmth, they are unpleasant when wet. Personally, I prefer a waterproof glove lined with thinsulate. The latter material is made of hollow fibres which, although thin, has exceptional heat-retention properties. Ski gloves are also most useful with leather or synthetic outers.

DUVET JACKET

To keep warm in winter most people wear a fibre-filled jacket. Ten years ago down-filled jackets were extremely popular but were bulky, making one look like a "Michelin man". Today, down is still popular but expensive. I still prefer a down-filled jacket for its exceptional heat-retaining properties, but its one failing is, when wet, down loses its heat retention quality and one feels extremely cold in a wet, soggy jacket.

Partly to keep costs down and to solve the heat loss problem, most jackets are made from man-made fibres, such as polyester, hollofill and thinsulate. These are not nearly as bulky, and have a hood, hand-warmer pocket, elasticated cuffs, and often a waterproof outer shell.

THERMAL UNDERWEAR

Ten years ago such clothing was mentioned only in private. But today it is quite fashionable, in attractive colours and materials. The longjohns and tops are in soft fibres, allowing the moisture to 'wick' away to the outside, leaving you feeling comfortable. I only wear such clothing on exceptionally cold days or when skiing.

Basic Day Walk Gear

DAY PACK

Although you are out for only a few hours walking five or more miles, you will need to carry a minimum of equipment to ensure your safety. It is wrong to assume that a sunny day will continue unchanged all day. A storm or rain shower can descend within minutes. It is better to carry too much than be without. Your rucksack will weigh about 10/15 lbs..

A day pack is usually between 20 and 30 litre capacity and made from nylon or cordura. Generally one large compartment with at least one side pocket. More refined models have a pocket in the flap. Choose one with padded carrying straps, preferably with a cotton and padded back to cushion the contents from annoying you as you walk. A waist strap is useful and stops the sack from swaying, and can be used to attach pockets or camera bags.

Your basic needs for day-hiking (some items will be worn) are:–

CHECK LIST

Rucksack 30 litre capacity	
Boots	
2 Pairs of 80% woollen socks	
Breeches/shorts	
Pullover/fibre-pile jacket	
Anorak/wind jacket	
Waterproof cagoule	
Waterproof gaiters/overtrousers	
Woollen hat	
Gloves	
Guidebook	
Map — referably 1:25,000 scale	
Compass and whistle	
Food and snacks	
Water bottle/thermos flask	
First-aid kit	
Torch, Survival Blanket	
Emergency Food.	

Pembrokeshire Coast

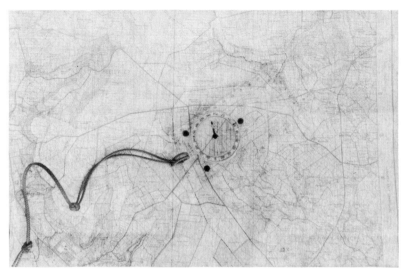

Map and Compass

MAP READING & COMPASS WORK

MAPS

We are lucky in Britain in having the Ordnance Survey, for no other country can match their quality and detail. For walking in the countryside the best map size is 1:25,000 (2½" to a mile). The major walking areas are in special — Outdoor Leisure series such as, The Peak District — White Peak; The Dark Peak and four maps covering the Lake District. Outside the principal areas the rest of the country is covered by the 1:25,000 O.S. Pathfinder series.

There is nothing mystical about a map. Opening one out is like opening a book on the area. At a glance you can see the villages, towns, houses, and sites of interest, and by looking at the contour lines you can see how steep or gradual the slopes of the hills are. The 1:25,000 series is exceptionally accurate for the walker, as they give the individual field boundaries and, like the 1:50,000 series, the public rights of way and long-distance footpaths are very clearly marked.

A study of the map symbols makes identification of items very easy and helps you to understand about the area you are walking in. As I walk I always have my map in my hand, folded on the area I am in. To protect your map from rain you can either keep it in a clear plastic map case or paint it with map preserver. By keeping it in your hand you can constantly check you are travelling the right way. By paying careful attention to the field patterns and special features, such as archaeological sites, you should not lose your way! There is no easy way to learn to read a map other than practice. In time it will become second nature, and eventually you will automatically know when you are walking the wrong way!

15

COMPASS

Even in rural countryside you should carry a compass. The best have a perspex base and revolving dial. There is nothing hard about taking a bearing, provided you know where you are! This is why it is most important to be accurate where you are, and why I always advocate carrying the map in your hand. Should you be in the mountains or moorlands and the clouds descend, there is no need to panic. Trust your compass.

Place the long edge of the compass on the point where you are and where you are heading for. While holding the compass in place, move the dial so that the north sign is pointing to the top of the map (which is also north). The grid lines and the lines on the base of the compass should be parallel. Lift the compass off and add on the magnetic variation as detailed on the map. Hold the compass in your hand and, when the compass north signs are together, follow the arrow direction on the perspex base — that is your line of travel.

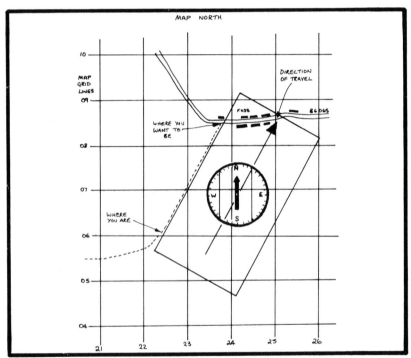

Compass diagram

Again it is practice that will make the exercise second nature.
Try it a few times in good weather to become proficient at it and to give you confidence in following the bearing. Unless in trackless country, work your bearings out to one mile intervals. Allow about 20 minutes to walk a mile. Having reached your next object, such as a white triangulation pillar, take another bearing for the next section. In time you will become very accurate and know exactly how long it should take you to reach the next destination.

Maps, Compass, Pedometer and Map-Measurer

HOW FAR WALKED

There are two small mechanical devices that are extremely useful and will give you a basic idea of how far you have walked and how far you are going to walk.

Map measurer — is a small hand wheel device which, when run across the line of your route, gives you an indication of the distance. The dial contains a needle and a scale of map sizes. Simply read the mileage number against your map size. The mileage will be reasonably accurate, but obviously the measurer cannot take in all the twists and turns of your pathline. Generally for every ten miles with a map measurer add on one mile.

Pedometer — is a pocket-sized watch-like instrument that can be clipped to your waist, side pocket or top pocket. As you walk along you activate a pendulum which records the distance YOU have walked. As a basic guideline, for every ten miles on the dial you will have covered about 9 map miles. The instrument is very accurate and records your own actual distance walked, but no-one walks in a straight line but always does little side trips to see items or when finding a stile, etc.. On the side of the dial is a sliding scale to record your stride length. The best way to work this out is to wet your feet and walk across a floor — naturally — and then measure the distance between your footprints. The average person's stride is 2½ feet.

Reference Book:

The Spur Book of Map and Compass — T. Brown and R. Hunter — Spurbooks 1979.

Day Snacks

DAY SNACKS

What one eats while out on a walk is a very personal choice. Many carry sandwiches and cakes, and a flask of coffee or soup. Others virtually nothing apart from a few bars of chocolate — like me! — while some rely on passing a pub for sandwiches and a drink. On New Year's Day I break my usual habit and carry a bottle of whisky, a chicken leg and an extra large hunk of Christmas cake!

Basically I just carry a few bars of chocolate — partly because I want instant energy, and partly because I prefer to keep going and not disrupt my walking rhythm. I have consumed as much as ten bars of chocolate in as many hours. In America I carry GORP, which is a mixture of raisins, nuts, coconut flakes and M. & M's (Smarties). These are all mixed together in a polythene bag, and one simply reaches in for a handful when necessary.

LIQUID

I break the accepted rule by not carrying water, even in 120oF. weather in a desert. The simple fact emerges — the more you drink, the more you want. Therefore I would rather abstain and will go without drinking for anything up to twelve hours. I don't encourage this as what you should do. I recommend you carry a liquid and drink sparingly.

FOOD CALORIFIC CHART

	Energy Value Calories per Ounce	Composition of Edible Portion		
		% Protein	% Carbohydrates	% Fats
CHEESE—				
Cheddar	113	25.0	32.2	2.1
Swiss	105	27.5	28.0	1.7
Processed	105	23.2	20.0	1.9
FRUIT—				
Orange	10	1.0	0	12.2
Banana	16	1.1	0	22.2
Apple (Raw)	13	0	0	12.0
Fig (Dried)	78	4.3	0	69.1
Raisin	82	2.5	0	77.4
FRUIT JUICES—				
Apple	13	0.1	0	11.9
Grape	19	0.2	0	16.6
Orange	14	0.7	0	10.4
Pineapple	16	0.4	0	13.5
Tomato	5	0.9	0	4.3
Orange Concentrate	63	4.1	0	50.7
NUTS—				
Almond	170	18.6	57.7	19.5
Brazil	185	14.3	66.9	10.9
Cashew	159	17.2	45.7	29.3
Coconut (Dried)	155	3.6	39.1	53.2
Peanut Butter	167	27.8	49.4	17.2
Peanut (Roasted)	165	26.0	49.8	18.8
Pecan	195	9.2	71.2	14.6
Walnut	158	14.8	64.0	15.8
CHOCOLATE—				
'Candy Bar'	141	9.2	25.3	59.6
Chocolate (Unsweetened)	143	10.7	53.0	28.9
Chocolate (Milk)	147	7.7	32.3	56.9
Chocolate (Sweet with Almonds)	151	9.3	35.6	51.3
Butterscotch	113	0.0	3.4	94.8
Caramel	113	4.0	10.2	76.6
Granulated Sugar	109	0.0	0	99.5
Plain Ice Cream	59	4.0	12.5	20.6

Great Gable — Lake District National Park.

WHERE TO WALK

The beauty of Britain is that wherever you live you are not far from the countryside — in fact you are never more than 80 miles from the sea. Even in cities there are endless opportunities with the city parks, heritage walks, and canal towpaths. In England and Wales there are ten National Parks of differing scenic attributes, from the coastal splendour of Pembrokeshire to the rugged beauty of North Wales or the Lake District. All contain a variety of walks from a short circular walk to a more demanding mountain day walk.

Walking should not be confined to National Parks, for there are numerous other areas, equally as good and scenic, such as the Areas of Outstanding Beauty. These include the Quantock Hills, the Lincolnshire Wolds and the Northumberland coast. There are the Heritage coasts, which include the Lizard Peninsula in Cornwall, the Gower Peninsula and Flamborough Head.

Equally as attractive, but more demanding, are the mountainous regions of England and Wales. Scotland too is superlative country, with the Trossachs, Glen Coe and Ben Nevis regions, and the Munroes to climb. The coastline is unspoilt and uncrowded, whilst off the west coast are the Inner and Outer Hebrides — a group of islands unequalled anywhere in the world.

In England and Wales are a huge number of both official and unofficial long-distance footpaths. The official ones include the renowned Pennine Way and Offa's Dyke Path. The unofficial, which have been created by individuals, include Wainwright's Coast to Coast path and my own Rivers' Way and Peak District High Level Route. There are also many day challenge walks, such as the Lyke Wake Walk and my own Challenge Walks. Scotland now has two official paths — The West Highland Way and the Southern Uplands Way.

In between the National Parks and scenic areas is a massive wealth of rural countryside, literally containing a latticework of public rights of way. My own county — Derbyshire — has 5,000 miles of rights of way, and in Britain there are more than 150,000 miles. The rural areas contain gentle walking across fields to hamlets or along canal towpaths. The opportunities are endless, and more than enough for a lifetime.

Glenashdale Waterfall — Isle of Arran

Gloves, Whistle and Torch

SAFETY AND SURVIVAL

Accidents happen frequently in the mountains, and largely because people don't go fully equipped. Additional to your walking clothes and rucksack you should carry:–
A small first-aid kit
An emergency blanket (silver foil or a large polythene bag)
Torch and Whistle
Emergency food, such as raisins or Kendal Mint cake.

These will ensure that you have food and protection for any emergency situation that could arise because of losing your way, if bad weather suddenly descends, or you find someone needing help.

Never hesitate to retreat if the weather turns bad; it is better to be safe than sorry. Always set off early in the mountains and be descending by early afternoon.

In your own interests it is advisable to let someone know where you are going and your expected time of return. Give yourself a good margin of time, for it would be embarrassing if a rescue team was alerted just because you spent longer on your walk than planned.

If there is an accident, there is an internationally recognised signal code — six flashes/blasts in one minute with a torch, mirror, whistle or white handkerchief. Followed by a minute's silence before repeating. The acknowledgment signal is three blasts/flashes in a minute.

You are recommended not to walk alone, but this is not always possible. A party of three is ideal, for one can stay with the injured while the other seeks help. Before one of you departs you must be certain of your location and work out a Grid Reference. There is nothing complicated about this, and every Ordnance Survey map details how this is done. The map is divided up into numbered kilometer squares. Simply note where you are and select the nearest line on your left (western) and record that number. Then in your mind divide the square into ten and work out how far you are from the left line. Then take the southern (bottom) line of your square. Record the number and work out from ten how far away you are.

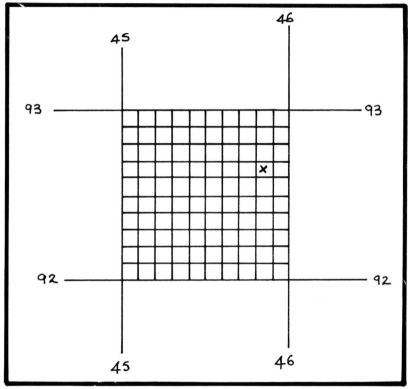

Grid Example

You should end up with a number like 459927. The 45 tells you your left (westerly) line and that you are close to line 46. The 927 tells you that your southern line is 92 and you are towards the 93 line mark.

The Ordnance Survey map will tell you your two letter prefix, ending up with a Grid Reference of SK459927. This enables you to inform the rescue party of your exact location, making their task of rescue much easier.

Reference Book:

First Aid for Hill Walkers and Climbers — J. Renouf and S. Hules — Penguin 1978.

WIND CHILL FACTOR

Until recently it was not fully appreciated how much the effect of wind reduced the temperature on exposed flesh. For instance, on a calm day at 50oF. the temperature is the same. If the wind speed is 25 m.p.h. the temperature has dropped to 30oF., and at 40 m.p.h. it is only 26oF. The following chart gives you an idea of how serious it can be in cold windy conditions, and gives added reason why, even on a summer's day, you should be properly equipped.

Wind
Speed
m.p.h.

Chill Factor — temperature on exposed flesh

0	50	40	35	30	25	20	15	10	5	0	−5	−10	−15	−20
5	48	37	32	27	21	16	10	6	0	−5	−10	−15	−21	−26
10	40	28	21	16	9	2	−2	−9	−15	−22	−27	−31	−38	−45
15	36	22	16	11	1	−6	−11	−18	−25	−33	−40	−45	−51	−60
20	32	18	12	3	−4	−9	−17	−24	−32	−40	−46	−52	−60	−68
25	30	16	7	0	−7	−15	−22	−29	−37	−45	−52	−58	−67	−75
30	28	13	5	−2	−11	−18	−26	−33	−41	−49	−56	−63	−70	−78
35	27	11	3	−4	−13	−20	−27	−35	−43	−52	−60	−67	−72	−83
40	26	10	1	−4	−15	−22	−29	−36	−45	−54	−62	−69	−76	−87
	50	40	35	30	25	20	15	10	5	0	−5	−10	−15	−20

Air temperature — Fahrenheit

Walking in Chatsworth Park — Peak District National Park

REMEMBER AND FOLLOW THE COUNTRY CODE

Enjoy the countryside and respect its life and work.

Guard against all risk of fire.

Fasten all gates.

Keep your dog under close control.

Keep to public paths across farmland.

Use gates and stiles to cross fences, hedges and walls.

Leave livestock, crops and machinery alone.

Take your litter home — pack it in — pack it out.

Help to keep all water clean.

Protect wildlife, plants and trees.

Take special care on country roads.

Make no unnecessary noise.

RANDOM GUIDE BOOK LIST —

National Guides —

A.A. Book of Country Walks
Walker's Britain Ordnance Survey/Pan Books 1982
Walker's Britain Ordnance Survey/Pan Books 1986
The Drinkers' Guide to Walking Proteus Publishing 1980
Britain's National Parks Ed. Mervyn Bell David & Charles 1979
Walking Through Northern England C.Emett & M.Hitton David & Charles 1982
Walking Through Wales D. & K. MacInnes David & Charles 1984
Walking Through Scotland D. & K. MacInnes David & Charles 1981
Ramblers' Ways Ed. D. Sharp David & Charles 1980
The Mountains of England and Wales G. Bridge West Col 1973
The Footpaths of Britain M. Marriott Queen Anne Press 1981

Lake District —

Seven guides by A. Wainwright published by the Westmorland Gazette — The
Eastern Fells
— The Far-Eastern Fells
— The Central Fells
— The Southern Fells
— The Northern Fells
— The North-Western Fells
— The Western Fells
Walks in the Lake District   Elizabeth Cull — Spurbooks 1979.

Yorkshire Dales —
Rambles in the Dales — Ramblers' Association — F. Warne 1979
Afoot in the Yorkshire Dale — H.O. Wade — Spurbooks 1981
Walks in the Limestone Country — A. Wainwright — Westmorland
    Gazette 1972
Walks on the Howgill Fells — A. Wainwright — Westmorland
    Gazette 1972

Cotswolds —
Discovering Walks in the Cotswolds — R. Kershaw and B. Robson —
    Shire Publications 1974.
Family Walks in the Cotswolds G Ottewell Scarthin Books 1986

Exmoor —
Walks in Exmoor — C. Green — Spurbooks 1981.

Dartmoor —
Walk Dartmoor — P. Tavy — Bartholomew 1984.

Walking & Backpacking advice books —

Hill Walking P.Williams Pelham Books 1979
Rambling Complete F.Duerden Kaye & Ward 1979
Britain At Your Feet D.Wickers & A. Pedersen Kogan Page 1980

OTHER BOOKS BY JOHN N. MERRILL
PUBLISHED BY JNM PUBLICATIONS

DAY WALK GUIDES —

SHORT CIRCULAR WALKS IN THE PEAK DISTRICT
LONG CIRCULAR WALKS IN THE PEAK DISTRICT
CIRCULAR WALKS IN WESTERN PEAKLAND
SHORT CIRCULAR WALKS IN THE STAFFORDSHIRE MOORLANDS
PEAK DISTRICT TOWN WALKS
SHORT CIRCULAR WALKS AROUND MATLOCK
SHORT CIRCULAR WALKS IN THE DUKERIES
SHORT CIRCULAR WALKS IN SOUTH YORKSHIRE
SHORT CIRCULAR WALKS AROUND DERBY
SHORT CIRCULAR WALKS AROUND BUXTON
HIKE TO BE FIT....STROLLING WITH JOHN
THE JOHN MERRILL WALK RECORD BOOK

CANAL WALK GUIDES —

VOL ONE — DERBYSHIRE AND NOTTINGHAMSHIRE
VOL TWO — CHESHIRE AND STAFFORDSHIRE

DAY CHALLENGE WALKS —

JOHN MERRILL'S PEAK DISTRICT CHALLENGE WALK
JOHN MERRILL'S YORKSHIRE DALES CHALLENGE WALK
JOHN MERRILL'S NORTH YORKSHIRE MOORS CHALLENGE WALK
PEAK DISTRICT END TO END WALKS
THE LITTLE JOHN CHALLENGE WALK
JOHN MERRILL'S LAKELAND CHALLENGE WALK

MULTIPLE DAY WALKS —

THE RIVERS' WAY
PEAK DISTRICT HIGH LEVEL ROUTE
PEAK DISTRICT MARATHONS
THE LIMEY WAY
THE PEAKLAND WAY

HISTORICAL GUIDES —

DERBYSHIRE INNS
100 HALLS AND CASTLES OF THE PEAK DISTRICT & DERBYSHIRE
TOURING THE PEAK DISTRICT AND DERBYSHIRE BY CAR
DERBYSHIRE FOLKLORE
LOST INDUSTRIES OF DERBYSHIRE
PUNISHMENT IN DERBYSHIRE
CUSTOMS OF THE PEAK DISTRICT AND DERBYSHIRE
WINSTER — A VISITOR'S GUIDE
ARKWRIGHT OF CROMFORD
TALES FROM THE MINES by GEOFFREY CARR

JOHN'S MARATHON WALKS —

TURN RIGHT AT LAND'S END
WITH MUSTARD ON MY BACK
TURN RIGHT AT DEATH VALLEY
EMERALD COAST WALK